THE FORCE OVERSLEEPS

Jarrett J. Krosoczka

Scholastic Inc.

For Monte Belmonte and his theatrical Padawans—Atticus, Enzo, and Pax

This book wouldn't have happened if it weren't for the dedication by the following people: Thank you to Michael P., Rick, Sam, Debra, and the entire team at Scholastic for shepherding this along and entrusting me with the lightsaber. Much love to Michael S., Jennifer, and the entire team at Lucasfilm for allowing me the honor to play around in a galaxy far, far away. Thank you to Jeffrey Brown for originating this fantastic series. Big thanks goes to Joey Weiser for his invaluable help in shading this book. Thank you to Rebecca Sherman. And for their patience and love, Gina, Zoe, Lucy, and Xavier Krosoczka.

Scholastic Children's Books,
Euston House, 24 Eversholt Street,
London NW1 1DB, UK

A division of Scholastic Ltd
London ~ New York ~ Toronto ~ Sydney ~ Auckland
Mexico City ~ New Delhi ~ Hong Kong

First published in the US by Scholastic Inc, 2017
First published in the UK by Scholastic Ltd, 2017
This edition published 2018

ISBN 978 1407 18839 3

A CIP catalogue record for this book is available from the British Library.

Printed by CPI Group (UK) Ltd, Croydon, CR0 4YY
Papers used by Scholastic Children's Books are made from wood grown in sustainable forests.

2 4 6 8 10 9 7 5 3

This is a work of fiction. Names, characters, places, incidents and dialogues are products of the author's imagination or are used fictitiously. Any resemblance to actual people, living or dead, events or locales is entirely coincidental.

www.starwars.com
www.scholastic.co.uk

A long time ago in a galaxy far, far away....

Victor Starspeeder, Jedi Academy's most awesomest student, stood behind the closed curtain. This was his big moment—his debut as the star of the annual musical.

The curtains swung open, and the audience erupted with applause! Victor sang his heart out, hitting every note.

He delivered his lines with swagger, and then—the big moment. The kiss he would share with his costar, Maya.

Victor leaned in, but then . . .

evil droids attacked!

8

Hexaday

Sometimes I hate how my sister, Christina, knows me so well. But I didn't write Maya five hundred holomessages over break, it was more like one hundred. Maybe two hundred. But, when Maya didn't write me back, I thought maybe something was wrong. I mean, it couldn't be me. Who wouldn't want to be holopals with me? Maya must have been super busy because she barely even logged on to our holochats for book club.

I mean, okay, all right, I know she was super busy based on her Stargram posts. She seemed to be enjoying herself . . .

Heptaday

I'm so stoked for my second year at Jedi Academy. It'll be so much better than last year for a number of reasons. For one, I get to start at the beginning of the year. And for two, I know who my friends are. And I have some great ones. Coleman, Emmett, Maya, Artemis, and I have, like, the perfect group. I love it just the way that it is. Also—I am now a second-year student, so I can't wait to have kids that are younger than me around. They'll totally look up to me.

Then there's the annual musical. I remember thinking the drama club would be totally lame, but the theater thing is actually a ton of fun. And I'll be there early enough to audition for a part this year. I don't see how they wouldn't make me the star.

EDITED BY THE STUDENTS OF JEDI ACADEMY Vol. MXVI #3

WELCOME BACK, YOUNGLINGS!

The faculty and staff at Jedi Academy eagerly await your return to Coruscant! Upon your arrival, please report immediately to your bunks. You will have so much catching up to do with your friends! We know that you will be tempted to venture out and explore the surrounding area, but we urge you all to stay on campus. While there have been rumors of Sith activity over the break, Principal Mar would like to assure everyone that they are just that—rumors. When asked for a further explanation, Master Yoda said, "Thieves and vandals roam Coruscant streets, not Sith. Hmmm. On the rise, crime may be. But no match for a Jedi a petty thief will be. All younglings have much work to do to become Jedi, yes? Your studies shall be prioritized. Stick to campus, you shall."

Please make sure that all forms are signed and handed in to your student advisor before the first day of classes.

ASK MS. CATARA!

Dear Ms. Catara,

As excited as I am to see my friends again, I'm sort of nervous about the new school year. And not just because of these Sith rumors. What if my friends suddenly decide that they don't like me? Am I being silly?

Signed,
An Anxious Second Year

Dearza Anxious Second Year,

It's A-OK to have fears, but don't let them overwhelm you. Youza entering a new year, and that iz an exciting times! If your friends are youz friends, you'll have nothing to worries about. And glad to hear that the Sith rumors aren't a bothering you.

XO,
Ms. Catara

HUTTFIELD

GALAXY FEED

7 Signs
That Sith
Are Lurking
Around
Coruscant

Six Easy
Steps to
Resist the
Dark Side

Super-Easy
Cake Recipes

Heptaday (continued)

Man, so weird that there is even talk about some dark side stuff happening anywhere near Jedi Academy. It's just insane to even think about. What dummy Sith would dare step anywhere near a school that is filled with so many powerful Jedi? I know that all of our teachers want us to think that there aren't Sith running around, but what if there are? What if they wanted to recruit new kids? I remember when I was a little kid, we'd be handed these flyers at our annual health checkup. They were super scary, but I never thought I'd ever need to worry about being anywhere near a dark side anything. Eh . . . I'm not worried. There's so much talent at Jedi Academy. And my crew and me? We wouldn't let them anywhere near us.

The dark side and YOU!

Don't become a statistic.

Student Name: Victor Starspeeder
Level: Padawan
Semester: Three
Homeroom: Master Yoda

CLASS SCHEDULE

0730-0850: ADVANCED USING THE FORCE
Master Yoda will build on the lessons learned in Year One.

0900-0950: STARPILOT FLIGHT TRAINING PART 1
Mr. Zefyr will introduce students to the basic concepts of piloting a starship.

1000-1050: PHYSICAL EDUCATION
Kitmum will push students to compete in various sports games.

1100-1150: HYPERALGEBRA
Mrs. Pilton will enforce various math equations on the students, perhaps some will prove helpful.

1200-1300: LUNCH BREAK

1300-1350: HISTORY OF THE JEDI ORDER
If we don't understand the past, we are doomed to repeat it.

1400-1450: GALACTIC GEOGRAPHY
Principal Mar will lead an in-depth study on how the singular ecosystems of our galaxy relate to one another.

1500-1550: PERSUASIVE DISCOURSE
Whether arguing with your best friend or before the Galactic Senate, Jedi must be able to make their case.

Heptaday (continued)

I so remember being the new kid like it was just a few MONTHS ago. It isn't easy. You don't know where things are, you don't have any friends yet, and it's like everybody is ahead of you in your classes. I know that it was really, really nice of me, but I helped the new kid find his way around the school. That's just the kind of guy that I am. Zavyer seems like a cool kid. Plus, it'll be good for me to have somebody around that is even newer than I am. A good reminder to everyone that good ol' Vic isn't the newbie! I didn't mean to show off, but I carried both of our bags using the Force. He seemed pretty impressed.

26

Monoday

I had every intention to put my best foot forward. But it turns out that in order to do that, you need to wake up on time and get to class when it starts. I don't understand why my friends didn't wake me up as they were headed out to class. And I can't even believe that Zavyer kid that they all loved is in my Force class. Apparently, this guy gets to skip a whole bunch of courses because he is so ahead of his peers. Then why, when I used the Force to carry his bags, did he seem so amazed? Was he trying to hide something?

The rest of my day wasn't so bad, I guess. It was great to see Mr. Zefyr again. And by great to see him, I mean he was as mean and as tough a teacher as ever! But here's something exciting—we're going to learn how to fly starships this semester! Can't you picture it? I'm going to look so good in that pilot's uniform. Mr. Zefyr insists that first semester is all about learning the basics and that there is no way that he would let us anywhere near an actual cockpit, but still. A guy can dream, right?

I hadn't run into Maya yet. We don't have many classes together. But I know that I'll see her at the first Drama Club meeting. I have only one goal in mind: Play. It. Cool.

31

Duoday

Why was Maya so surprised that I'd want to audition for a part? Does she not think I have what it takes? At least she was happy to see me. That was pretty cool. MS. Catara tried telling me that it might be too much to both act in the play and design the sets.

Youza burdenin' youzeself. Yourza schoolwork will suffer!

But I can handle it. How hard can it be to memorize a few lines and pretend to be somebody else? Easy.

And it looks like I'll be spending a lot more time with Zavyer. T-3PO signed us both up as set designers. Which is great, because Xander is just the very best!*

*Ugh, okay. I am not so sure he is the very best. Does he really need to have drawing skills like me, too?

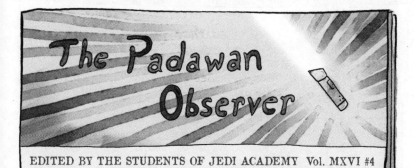

The Padawan Observer

EDITED BY THE STUDENTS OF JEDI ACADEMY Vol. MXVI #4

SEMESTER STARTS WITH STYLE!

The first semester is in full swing as new students adjust to life at Jedi Academy! By now, everyone should be familiar with how to navigate around the corridors. And remember, if you have any questions, ask a protocol droid. They're here to help! To all students new and returning, please remember to report any suspicious activity that you might see directly to Principal Mar.

FRIENDLY REMINDER

P-10 would like to remind everyone to put litter in its proper receptacles. While it is his primary function to keep the grounds in tip-top shape, it is not his primary function to pick up after you. Your parents' droid does not operate here.

ASK MS. CATARA!

Dear Ms. Catara,

I have this new friend, and he's nice and all, but he's totally getting in my way. I mean, all of the things that I am good at and known for—he's really good at too. I'm nervous that all of my friends are going to like him better.

Signed,
I Was Here First

Dearza You Waz Heres First,

Well, first of allz, jealousy is an ugly emotion. For all youza knows, this friend of yours is jealous of you! And wouldn't that make you feel sad for them? Maybe they really look up to you, and you can't even seez that because you are blinded by your own emotions?

Thinks about its!
XO,
Ms. Catara

37

Quadday

My sister can be a weirdo—most people probably think that about their siblings. But truth be told, I love Christina and I think she is super smart. Maya was right, though, it was odd to see her chilling by herself all the time. She usually doesn't want me around because I embarrass her in front of her friends. (It's way fun to egg her on.) But now that she isn't around her friends much at all, I can't figure out why she won't stop to talk with me in the halls.

Classes continue to get more intense. I like not being the youngest at the school, but, man, they just pile on the responsibilities as you get older! I feel like I spend all my waking hours working on homework for my classes. Or thinking about work for classes. Or worrying about getting into trouble for forgetting to do the work for classes. Which probably explains why I love getting to bed to sleep and turning my brain off for a little bit. Only problem is, my bed is so comfortable that I continue to oversleep. And as much as my bunkmates prod me to get up and out, I never seem to make it out of bed in time. But that Elara girl has been super helpful. Before she heads to class, she double-checks to see if I'm ready. And we like talking about the same things, so that's cool.

You're pretty great at everything, Victor.

GALAXY FEED

Creative
Lightsabers
That Will
Leave You
Speechless

Top 8
Vacation
Planets

Considering
a Loth-
cat For a
Pet? Think
Again!

Pentaday

T–3PO and RW–22 selected the annual musical. The Drama Club will be putting on a production of *Little Sarlacc of Horror.* And they posted the cast list. And who's playing the lead? You'd think I was, but no. I didn't even get a named part. I am Villager number two. Number TWO! That means that there is somebody a level ahead of me in the bit-part department. So who did get the lead you ask? Yup. You've guessed it . . . the new kid, Zavyer. I think that the entire galaxy is conspiring against me. I thought Coleman would be mad that he didn't get the lead again this year, but he was totally cool with it. He is going to voice the giant sarlacc puppet. Maya also got a major part, but there's no surprise there. She lives for this kind of stuff. She's also the president of Drama Club, so . . .

Tough break, Victor.

Monoday

Today in class, Yoda presented our annual planet study. This year, our class will be focusing on Wutooine. Just about every important starship in the galaxy gets manufactured there. It's also home to the skyhopper tracks.

When we go on our field trip, I'm hoping we get to see some of the races. Yoda told us that since we are learning how to fly ships we ought to know how they are put together. Well, he actually said something along the lines of . . .

Put together ships you shall know, hmmm? Fly them around you shall have the knowledge, something, something, something . . . Hmmmm?

It's hard to remember anything Yoda says when you are so busy trying to decipher what he's saying!

My dad was really good at fixing up old ships. At least that's what Christina always said. Maybe someday I'll get a handle on how to do all of that technical stuff like my pops. Maybe I'll even get to design some new starships myself. It would be like designing sets for school plays, but way more complicated.

V-Wing fighter.
("V" for Victor!)

49

Jedi Academy 164th

Lightsaber Fencing Tournament

Per tradition, all will try out,
top ten will compete!

Triday

I've been stoked about the lightsaber tournament since I saw Dad's old trophy in the garage back on Naboo. Mom didn't much like keeping Dad's stuff around, but she told me that the trophy reminded her of happier times. He'd be so proud to know that I'm entering the lightsaber tournament and even prouder when I bring home the trophy for myself!

FIRST PLACE
EDWARD
STARSPEEDER

If only he could be here to share in the excitement. I know that he'd be one of those dads who came to every single school event, like Coleman's dad. Coleman thinks his dad is sort of annoying. But he has no idea how lucky he is to have that kind of enthusiasm around. Okay, maybe his dad could turn up with fewer corny posters . . .

Colemania is contagious

One of the less embarassing signs from Mr. Flytrap →

Hexaday

Coleman and Emmett can't seem to get enough of Zavyer. They invite him over to our room every night to play holochess. I'm not a big fan of holochess. I just don't see the point of it. Artemis says that's because I haven't taken the time to really learn the strategy. I watch my friends play, but I just can't catch on to it. Zavyer is really good at it and he offered to teach me how to play. He said he could bring his travel set for the flight to Wutooine.

I suppose I could try and let him teach me. But that would of course mean more time with Zavyer. But I guess we were going to be stuck on this field trip together anyhow.

Duoday

It was a long trip to Wutooine. Understandably, nobody was very excited to talk to me after that dig I gave Zavyer. But you know who didn't hold a grudge? Zavyer. Man, that guy is even really good at being nice. He taught me a few of the basics of holo chess. I was grateful to finally see that we were making our initial approach to Wutooine. I was very much looking forward to stretching my legs and getting off that ship!

I probably would have been better off riding on top of the ship!

Triday

Well, I guess Zavyer isn't half bad after all. I knew I liked that guy from the moment I first met him! We all stayed up well past lights out, talking about all sorts of things. Our lives back home, our families, and the upcoming semester break. Turns out Zavyer and I have more in common than I realized. His parents split a few years back, and he's only seen his dad a few times since. That can't be easy. I know Russell can get on my nerves sometimes, and he'll never replace my dad, but I am glad that he's around.

We were all really sleepy on the morning of the skyhopper race. As tired as I was, nothing could stop me for being totally amped for this. I've been drawing skyhoppers since I was a little kid.

I drew this when I was 4

65

Quadday

Ah, man! The races were even more exciting than I could have possibly dreamed. Holos can make you feel like you are right there, but nothing beats actually being there in real life. The smell of the exhaust, the roaring thunder of the crowds, the taste of meatlumps . . . it all added up to an unbelievable experience.

Afterward, we got to meet some of the racers and get their autographs. I'll post a few of them here in my journal. We went on to tour some of the factories that produced these incredible machines. I think over the upcoming semester break, I'm going to try my hand at making my own skyhopper model.

70

71

Hexaday

It was a long flight back to Naboo. Christina wasn't especially chatty, no surprise there. My datapad's battery ran out, so I read all of the school newspapers, which left me alone with my thoughts. Yoda was pretty confident that something was bothering me. And I guess he was right. Not that it was something that I didn't want to talk about, but more something that I didn't know that I needed to talk about. Those T-16 skyhoppers that I saw on Wutooine inspired me. They also totally made me think about my dad. He would think that it was so cool that I was having these experiences. If he was there to greet me when we got back home, he would totally help me build my own model, maybe we would even work on a real, full-scale version.

73

74

Heptaday

Vacation came and went, and it was time to travel back to Jedi Academy. Christina was so aloof the entire time we were home, even more than usual. She didn't even have any holochats with her girlfriends from school. Eavesdropping on those chats are usually my favorite things about being home with Christina. My sister's older friends are mysterious beings. Any time I asked Christina what was up, she just ignored me completely. Even here, on the flight back, she is keeping her lips sealed. I thought about what Yoda said, about needing to talk to somebody to get your feelings out. I wish I knew what she was bottling up. And I wish she would talk to me. And since she has made it abundantly clear that she's not interested in hearing about those T-16 skyhoppers, I opened up a program on my datapad that makes fart noises. If you can't help your sister, annoy her!

The Padawan Observer

EDITED BY THE STUDENTS OF JEDI ACADEMY Vol. MXVI #5

EXCITING DAYS AHEAD!

Who is ready for a fresh start in the new semester? We here at *The Padawan Observer* are excited about a lot of fantastic events that are coming up at Jedi Academy. The annual alumni weekend is around the corner. So don't be surprised if some middle-aged Jedi are really excited to see their old dorms. As Yoda says, "Nostalgia is strong with these former students." If you haven't already signed up for the annual Lightsaber Tournament, be sure to see Mr. Zefyr before week's end.

What are you most looking forward to in the lightsaber tournament?

"The lightsabers."
-Victor, 2nd year

"Meeting the alumni."
-Nara, 3rd year

"Waaargh!"
-Kitmum, P.E.

ASK MS. CATARA!

Dear Ms. Catara,

Longtime reader, first time writer. I consider myself pretty tough, but my spirits are down. My friends have been super mean to me. They don't include me in things, and I'm pretty sure that they are saying mean things behind my back. I can't even deal. But how do I deal?

Signed,
Perplexed Padawan

Dearza Perplexed Padawan,

My, my, my. It a sounds like youza gots yourself a tough situation. I says, it's a big school, and youza should find yourself new friends. It is not fair for anybody to be spreading lies about youza. Youza should report them to a teacher, or come see me in the guidance office.

I am a here to helps!
Xo,
Ms. Catara

Monoday

I could not believe what P-10 showed me on Stargram. How could Christina's friends be so mean? What happened last semester to make her friendships fall apart like this? My sister is not a Sith! She can be tough on me, sure. I tease her about the Dork Side, yes. But she doesn't have a dark bone in her body. I can see why my friends were trying to protect me from these posts, but if my sister is being cyberbullied, I want to know about it! I was determined to get to the bottom of it. I headed down to her dorm room, even though P-10 tried to stop me. He thought it best I wait to calm down a bit. I ran to Christina's dorm with P-10 rolling behind me. Christina's so-called friends weren't around and neither was she. I closed my eyes and cleared my mind as best I could and searched my feelings. The gym. She was working off some steam, I was sure of it.

Force-sensitive siblings have a special connection.

85

Duoday

Artemis and I were on our way to Drama Club when I couldn't help but feel that people were looking at me differently in the hallway. They'd get all quiet when we walked by and then whisper when we passed. I'd hear things like, "Did you hear about his sister?" and "That's the Sith's younger brother." Those holos posted to Stargram were starting to go viral around school and people were falling for it! It made me think of how I treated Artemis at the beginning of last year. It was so unfair of me to make assumptions about him based on my perceptions. Now, I truly know how rotten it feels when people pass around rumors. When we arrived at Drama Club, everyone was chattering away, but fell silent at the sight of me. Then they avoided eye contact. That was awkward. Are my friends all falling for this garbage? The only person who came right up to me was Zavyer. He gave me a big high five and we looked over our sketches for the set design. We have to make a giant sarlacc puppet. It's going to be a challenge, but it will be a good distraction from all the messiness.

Yoda sent out holomail to every student at Jedi Academy.
I guess those Stargrams made it to the faculty.

Fall prey to gossip, do not.
Respect one another, you will. Give
everyone a chance, you must! A true
Jedi believes not everything they
read on Stargram. Hmmm. Search
for the facts, the sources check, and
with an understanding heart and
open mind, the truth will find you.
May the Force be with you.

HOLOMAIL

Quadday

Mr. Zefyr said that he was going to be charitable
with us and not punish us for wandering so far
away. I think that he only did that because Artemis
was with me. If it was just me, I'm sure Mr. Zefyr
would have gladly given me detention for the rest of
the year. As hard as I tried, I couldn't explain to Mr.
Zefyr why we were there. He's always made it clear
that he does not want to hear excuses, he wants
to see action. But I'm so sad right now, journal.
Because you know what? I think that my sister
is collaborating with a legit Sith. I know that she
sensed my presence and then used the Force to shoo
Artemis and me away. She's gotten real STRONG. I
mean, Artemis, me, AND P-10, that's a lot of weight
to move, and to do so without even really looking?

I don't even know what to think anymore. It's like
my world has been flipped upside down. Could all of
those rumors be true? Christina Starspeeder—on the
way to the dark side? I just can't even. And if she is
walking down a dark path, how do I stop her?

GALAXY FEED

How to Have Conflict-Free Talks with Your Siblings

What's New in Helmet Fashion

What Speeder Is Right for You?

Really, though? I see everything that's been going on around school.

Okay, I'm worried about my sister.

She's really all I've got, aside from my mom. And Russell, I guess. But Russell has only been around for a few years.

Family can be tough, for sure. I rarely see my dad. And I haven't really seen my big brother at all since our parents split up.

What? I thought you were Mr. Perfect Everything.

You didn't look close enough, I guess.

Sarlacc is looking awesome, guys!

Well, duh, Victor is working on it.

Hexaday

I am running out of things to say to kids in the hallway who ask me about Christina. I continue to stick up for her, but it's hard to when I'm starting to believe that maybe they're right and I'm wrong. What happened? Was she angry that Dad was gone? Was she bored with her schoolwork? She's the smartest person I know. Ms. Catara told me that as much as I wanted to help, I also needed to focus on my studies. Principal Mar was not too pleased that I had skipped out on the test, yet he didn't even give me a detention. He did make me take the test that same day, so I still didn't get to study. Unless my guesses were spot-on, I probably flunked.

What species is indigenous to Kashyyyk?
A) Ewoks
B) Gungans
C) Wookiees
D) Hutts

This peaceful planet is known for its picturesque landscapes.
A) Trandosha
B) Ithor
C) Naboo
D) Bespin

This planet serves as a connector between the Outer and Inner Rims.
A) Ord Mantell
B) Glee Anslem
C) Iridonia
D) None of the Above

When in doubt, select C!

Mr. Zefyr pulled me aside in Lightsaber Dueling class and said that while he appreciated my enthusiasm, I needed to remain calm, especially in the midst of a lightsaber duel. Apparently, I freaked out Emmett, which I guess isn't saying much—he is startled easily. But Mr. Zefyr sensed the rage boiling within me. "Save that aggression for Kitmum's sports games," he grumbled. From watching holos about Jedi, I would assume that it was all about aggression, but Mr. Zefyr pointed to a quote from Yoda that he had hanging up on the wall of his classroom.

Your homework is to meditate and clear your thoughts, Starspeeder!

"You will know the good from the bad when you are calm, at peace."
—Yoda

The Padawan Observer

EDITED BY THE STUDENTS OF JEDI ACADEMY   Vol. MXVI #6

ALUMNI WEEKEND BRINGS YOU JEDITALKS!

It's that time of year again! Jedi Academy is so proud to welcome back cherished members of our alumni community. Whether you are celebrating your first reunion or your two hundredth, the students have so much to learn from you. Students, we encourage you to check out some of the wonderful lectures we have lined up for you. All JediTalks will happen in the auditorium unless otherwise noted in the schedule. Students participating in the lightsaber tourney, please see Mr. Zefyr to go over protocol.

WEEKEND HIGHLIGHTS:

- Tour the updates of our cafeteria!

- Meet up with old classmates at the Jedi mixer.

- Shop the Jedi Academy store for official Jedi Academy–branded robes!

JEDITALKS

Schedule

0730
"In My First 600 Years, Learned I Have"
Speaker: Yoda

0830
"Designing Your Destiny"
Speaker: Argo Chum Chum

0930
"Communication Without Lightsabers"
Speaker: Kinstar Badara

1030
"So You Want to Be a Jedi Knight?"
Speaker: Karly Panchoo

1130
"Sensing Beyond Your Senses"
Speaker: Lars Stranom

1230
"Using Jedi Mind Tricks to Affect Change"
Speaker: Okul

1330
"Robes Make Not a Jedi Great"
Speaker: Kwon Lee

Pentaday

Christina knew just what she was doing when she called me a nerf herder. I didn't care about the Lightsaber Tournament trophy as much as I wanted her to take back the nerf herder crack. I really didn't expect to win. When I saw that I would have to face Christina, I figured she'd beat me. But there was, like, this voice in my head egging me on. I've never experienced that before. It was weird. "Clear your mind, a Jedi must," is something that Yoda says all the time. But I thought he meant things like thinking about ice cream and cake and things like that. I thought my obsessing over T-16 skyhoppers was the problem. Is it even possible to have thoughts in your brain that aren't yours? Ugh! Middle school is so confusing.

Duoday

It's the end-of-year crunch. All my final exams are coming up and all my essays are due. Artemis kept reminding me that I should have started working on these a long, long time ago, but I've had a few things on my plate. But anyhow, how hard could it be to write a five-page essay on the ramifications of trade deals on local famers on Tatooine? That essay is just going to write itself.

Elara has been coming by to offer to be my study buddy. It's nice enough of her, but I find that every time I take out my datapad to read up on molecular biology in sentient beings, I end up scrolling over to news about what's happening in the world of skyhoppers. And really, what info will really help me in twenty years anyhow? The physical aspects of some species that I'll probably never encounter or the latest stats of who won what race and with what modifications made to their craft?

GALAXY FEED

Scroll Through the Holo Galleries from Alumni Weekend at Jedi Academy!

Lessons from JediTalks, From the Wonderful to the Absurd!

Skyhopper Racer Doesn't Turn Up for Race. Krio Vin's Whereabouts a Mystery.

Quadday

T-3PO and RW-22 are short-circuiting—literally! Their
motherboards can't handle the stress and pressure
running on their motors with the musical's opening
night approaching. The sarlacc puppet that Zavyer
and I rigged up needs a little work. It's meant to fit
over Coleman, who plays the part of the carnivorous
creature. But it needs a few modifications . . .
Coleman does need to be able to see out of the
costume . . .

I'm hungry!
Feed me!

Um, Cole.
I'm over
here.

Apparently, sight is integral to theater work.
I suggested Coleman just use the Force
to find his way around stage,
but T-3PO
didn't agree.

We're doomed!

Mr. Zefyr's final exam will be interesting. The good news is that I've managed to get through simulated flights without throwing up. It isn't as easy as you would think, but your body eventually gets used to all the motion and pressure. P-10 is certainly grateful that I'm keeping my food down—those simulators are hard to clean. (Never mind the helmets.) Also, they should never schedule that class after lunch.

Actually, out of all my exams, this is the one that I feel best about. I think that I am destined to work with these machines. They move fast and powerfully through the sky, which is pretty much me. Mr. Zefyr keeps saying that life isn't a skyhopper race, contemplation and quick thinking can mean all the difference between safe passage and obliteration. Mr. Zefyr can be so dramatic. You get used to it.

Student Name: Victor Starspeeder
Level: Padawan
Semester: Four

REPORT CARD

JEDI ACADEMY · CORUSCANT CAMPUS

CLASS	NOTES	GRADES
ADVANCED FORCE	Powerful, but patience needed!	B
STARPILOT FLIGHT TRAINING	Brave, bold, and foolish!	B+
PHYSICAL EDUCATION	*(scribbles)*	*(spiral)*
HYPER-ALGEBRA	I am glad this class is history	B
HISTORY OF THE JEDI ORDER	Was Victor even in my class ??	C—
GALACTIC GEOGRAPHY	Clear your mind!	B
PERSUASIVE DISCOURSE	Victor has potential to arrive on time.	B—

Monoday

Well, I didn't totally flunk out of Jedi Academy, so that's good. My teachers must have taken pity on me, because I felt so unprepared for all of my final exams. But I did learn a lot in my classes this year, even if I'm not sure that they will ever really help me when I'm a Jedi. Like, when I'm off saving the galaxy, will it really matter that I know how to solve algebraic equations? And with technology, do I really need to memorize where all the planets are and what section of the galaxy they're in? I'll just ask the navicomputer, it won't steer me wrong. The big annual school dance is coming up, but it's hard to get excited for it. I don't really have happy feet these days. Elara is insisting that I go, and well, she's been so helpful to me all year. It's the least I could do. That and . . . well, Elara is pretty cool. I'm going to miss seeing her so much over break. But she said that she'd have her family stop in at Naboo on their annual vacation.

Kinda, sorta OK after all.

137

Pentaday

Well, that was an emotional ride through a meteor shower. It turns out, my dad hasn't been dead all these years, he just went to the dark side and has been working the skyhopper race circuit. Now I understand why my mom was so concerned about me getting into these races—she didn't want me reconnecting with my father. Yoda assured me that all skyhopper racers aren't this seedy, so this shouldn't let my love of the spacecraft die. I'm so relieved to know that I wasn't losing Christina to the dark side. I am amazed by her bravery. Yoda and Mr. Zefyr were right to choose her over me. I had put my dad on such a pedestal, I would have been duped into thinking he was a good guy. I also have some work to do in regards to my self-control, but I'm getting there. I am, after all, at the best school in the entire galaxy.

I'm sad that the school year is ending; it's proven that I have the best friends to exist ever. But I can't wait to see Mom and Russell at home. I have a lot to thank them for. That couldn't have been easy for them to keep up this idea that my father was dead. It was easier for me to grow up thinking that he was just gone versus him being a bad man. And as much as I always wanted to know him, I did have a dad in Russell. It isn't about who you come from, but who surrounds you. And I sure am lucky to have the best parents I could have ever asked for.

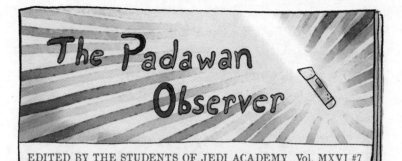

The Padawan Observer

EDITED BY THE STUDENTS OF JEDI ACADEMY   Vol. MXVI #7

GRADUATING STUDENT HAILED A HERO!

Christina Starspeeder, who is about to take her first steps beyond Jedi Academy as an alumni, is being heralded as a hero for having aided in a sting operation to vanquish a Sith. Working closely with Master Yoda and Mr. Zefyr, Ms. Starspeeder went undercover as an apprentice to one Krio Vin, pretending to be interested in the dark side of the Force. Through her diligence and the bravery of a group of second-year students, Krio Vin has been brought to justice and no longer poses a threat to the Jedi Academy community.

THE SHOW MUST GO ON!

The annual musical, *Little Sarlacc of Horror,* is set to be staged tonight in the Jedi Academy auditorium! There are still a few tickets left, so please send a holo to T-3PO or RW-22 in the theater office if you are interested!

Heptaday

Coleman absolutely killed it as the singing sarlacc. And I'm not just talking about what his character does on stage! (Sorry, spoiler alert!) I'm really proud of what Zavyer and I were able to do together by building that beast of a puppet. I managed to deliver my one line without falling on my face. Not as easy as one would think. My line lasted about two seconds, but the moments leading up to it felt like an eternity. I could feel my heart beat in my temples! Definitely gave me newfound respect for what Maya and Coleman do every year. How do you even memorize that many lines? On top of studying? They are mega geniuses, clearly.

Maybe I'll get a lead next year.

Mom and Russell will be arriving in the morning for Christina's graduation ceremony. It's going to be a big deal, because Christina will be getting a medal at the ceremony. Mom hasn't been on campus since Christina's first semester. When I transferred in, she wasn't able to make the trip, but she knew I had Christina to look out for me. I'm excited to show Mom my dorm and introduce her to my friends. I think that she'll really like them. (I mean, honestly, with the way she stresses about me, I think she'll be worried that I am a bad influence on them, not the other way around.)

hero

Christina gave this heartfelt speech at the awards ceremony. I think she was being complimentary of me. I asked her if I could keep her speech to post in my journal.

i have learned so much during my time here at Jedi Academy. Master Yoda, always a bright sage you were. Mr. Zefyr, your temper was only matched by your passion for education. But out of everyone who helped me, the most valuble people have been my family. Everything i ever needed to know about courage, i learned from watching my mother as she ensured a safe childhood for my brother and me. Everything i ever needed to know about compassion, i learned from my stepfather, Russell. And everything i learned about patience, i learned by dealing with my little brother, Victor.

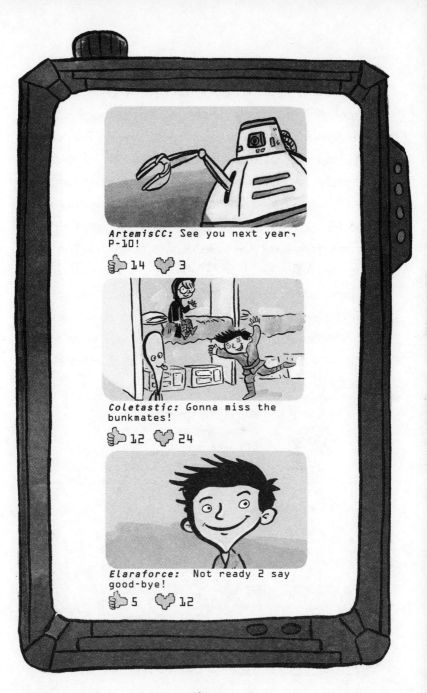

Duoday

Christina got her top choice for Jedi mentor, and it hit me—I'm not going to see my sister much at all next school year. I'm going to miss having her around Jedi Academy. Sure, she gives me the cold shoulder, but everyone has their own weird way of letting their family know that they love them. I wonder what kind of mentor I'll end up with. Artemis already has a spreadsheet of possible directions for him to take. He'll have his pick of mentors, his grades are so good. Coleman and Emmett keep talking about getting mentors that work together so they won't be far from each other. I'll take whoever will have me. I'll admit it—I can be difficult to manage. But I'm fun to be around.

Russell helped me pack my bags while Mom was in Christina's dorm helping her. I don't know how this happens, but I seem to accumulate so many things to bring home. (And I'm not just talking about that sarlacc puppet. We decided it would be best to stash that in the greenroom of the theater.) Russell was very helpful, though. He helped me stuff everything into my suitcase and sweep up my space. Even though I thought Russell could be lame at times, he is a man who turned up and helped. And he does love my mom, that is obvious. So even though he tells some super-lame jokes at times, I'm glad that he's around.

Russell helped me zip up my suitcase, and we didn't even need to use the Force.

EDITED BY THE STUDENTS OF JEDI ACADEMY Vol. MXVI #8

BON VOYAGE!

That is a wrap on another successful year at Jedi Academy. It is never a dull moment in these halls, and this year proved to be no exception. Whether you were training for the Lightsaber Tournament or memorizing lines for the annual musical, we hope that you feel good about your time at Jedi Academy. With the end of every year, we also must bid a bittersweet farewell to our graduating students. And what a remarkable group we have setting forth into the galaxy. You will certainly be hearing stories of the good deeds these future Jedi perform for years to come.

WHAT ARE YOU LOOKING FORWARD TO ON SEMESTER BREAK?

Artemis Oophanoe
Staying indoors and reading.

Maya Phoenix
Going to see shows.

Zavyer Kroff
Staying in touch with my new friends.

ASK MS. CATARA!

Dear Ms. Catara,

How do I handle this? I'm filled with so many conflicting emotions. I thought I liked this one girl, but she never gave me the time of day. But there is this other girl that I think might like me like me. I like her, but not necessarily like her like her. What do I do?

Signed,
Confused

Dearza Confused,

A Jedi musta clear theirs minds of such things. Love comes in all sorts of forms and shapes, like the world around us. My suggestion would be to justa make friends with everyonez. Young hearts are filled with so many confusing emotions. Just be kindz to one another and enjoy spending times with each other.

XO,
Ms. Catara

172

Jarrett J. Krosoczka is a *New York Times* bestselling author, a two-time winner of the Children's Choice Book Award for the Third to Fourth Grade Book of the Year, an Eisner award nominee, and is the author and/or illustrator of more than thirty books for young readers. His work includes several picture books, the Lunch Lady graphic novels, and Platypus Police Squad middle-grade novel series. Jarrett has given two TED Talks, both of which have been curated to the main page of TED.com and have collectively accrued more than two million views online. He is also the host of The Book Report with JJK on SiriusXM's Kids Place Live, a weekly segment celebrating books, authors, and reading.

Jarrett lives in Western Massachusetts with his wife and children, and their pugs, Ralph and Frank.